Grace and Wyatt's Fishin
By Shasta Sitton
Illustrated by Marvin Teeples

Whitetail Press, LLC

Copyright © 2017 Shasta Sitton

ISBN 978-0-9915571-3-4

Wyatt and Grace love visiting their grandparents. There are toys to play with, books to read, and lots of yummy food to eat.

Sometimes eating too much yummy food makes you tired. Wyatt and Grace decide they need a break.

"Hey, I have an idea," says Grandpa. "Let's go fishing!"
"Fishing? That sounds boring," says Wyatt.

"I have everything we need; rods, bait, and my trusty tackle box," says Grandpa proudly.

"Don't forget about me!" Grandma says as she comes out of the house wearing a floppy hat.

Wyatt has an idea. "Grandpa, I have a fishing video game. Why don't we play that today, and go fishing tomorrow?" Grandma chuckles and says, "Don't worry. Real fishing is much more fun than playing video games. Hop in and we'll go to the lake."

After a short drive, they arrive at a beautiful lake. Wyatt and Grace jump out of the truck.

The sun is shining, the birds are chirping, and the lake is as smooth as glass.

"Wow," says Grace. "It's pretty."

"Yeah, it is," agrees Wyatt. "Maybe this wasn't such a bad idea."

Grandma and Grandpa show Wyatt and Grace how to bait their hook, hold the rod, and cast. Grace quickly gets the hang of it, but Wyatt has a hard time casting. This is different than his fishing video game.

Wyatt tries again, and makes a nice cast into the lake.

Grandpa smiles and says, "Great job. Now, hold the rod really still. If your bobber goes under the water that means a fish is biting. Give your rod a small jerk to set the hook."

Wyatt and Grace both hold still. Suddenly, Grace sees her bobber move and go under the water.

"I got a bite! I got a bite!" Grace yells.

"Good job!" says Grandma. "Now, give your rod a little jerk, keep the tip in the air, and reel it in."

Grace's rod bounces and bobs as she reels in the fish. She smiles when it splashes its way to the surface. "I did it!" she yells.

"What a beautiful trout," says Grandma. She gets her hands wet and gently grabs the trout. She then shows Grace how to safely remove the hook.

"This trout is pretty young," Grandma says. "Let's release it, so it can get bigger. Maybe we can even catch it again someday."

Grace likes the sound of that.

"Since we're going to release the trout, it's important to keep it wet and hold it level. We don't want to hurt it," explains Grandma as she gently gives the trout to Grace.

"Wow," says Grace. She is surprised at how slimy and slippery the trout is. It wriggles and tries to get away.

Grace slowly lowers it to the water. As soon as she lets go, the trout swims away and disappears into the deep lake.

Wyatt wants to catch a fish too! He thinks maybe he should fish where Grace was instead. As he starts to reel in, he feels a tu on his line, and his bobber goes under the water.

"I got one!" Wyatt yells. He jerks his rod, and tries to reel, but it won't. The fish mus be huge!

He jerks his rod harder and harder until it finally breaks free. Wyatt looks up just in time to see a huge, green monster flying right toward him! He tries to duck, but...SPLAT! The green monster hits him right in the face!

"Help!" Wyatt screams as he wrestles with the green, slimy monster.

"Hold still, Wyatt," Grandpa chuckles. "I'll get those weeds off of you."

Weeds? Wyatt was sure it was a monster. But as he opens his eyes, he sees only green, slimy weeds. No monster at all. His hook must have gotten caught on the weeds as he reeled in.

"Oops!" Wyatt giggles.

Wyatt is now more determined than ever to catch a fish. He casts his line, and does his best to be patient.

Just as he's about to give up hope, his bobber disappears under the water. He gives his rod a small jerk and tries to reel in, but it won't. He must be snagged on weeds again.

Frustrated, Wyatt starts to ask Grandpa to help him get his line free. But before he can say anything, his line shoots to the left. Then it shoots to the right. The tip of his rod bends and jerks. Maybe he isn't snagged after all!

"Looks like you have a fish on!" says Grandpa. "Keep your tip up and reel in slowly. Don't force it or the line will break."

Wyatt reels and reels until, suddenly;
a gigantic trout jumps out of the water.
It lands with a big splash.
 "Wow!" Wyatt yells.
 "It's huge!" says Grace.

As soon as the trout is back underwater, it takes off swimming away from Wyatt. He now has to reel the trout in all over again.

Wyatt reels in the fish, and the fish swims away. He reels in again, and again the fish swims away. Wyatt is starting to get a little tired and frustrated, but he's not giving up!

Just when Wyatt thinks he's never going to get the trout to shore, he sees it near the top of the water. The beautiful trout looks as tired as Wyatt feels.

This gives Wyatt a burst of energy, and he reels as fast as he can. The trout glides to the shore, where it jumps and splashes.

Grandpa wades in and gently picks the trout up.

Wyatt did it! It took a lot of patience and work, but he finally caught the trout!
"It's huge!" says Wyatt.
"It sure is," says Grandpa with a smile. "I'm proud of you, Wyatt. You followed directions and didn't give up. This is a beautiful trout."
Grandpa removes the hook and hands the trout to Wyatt

The trout is very heavy. The scales are slippery and sparkle in the sun. Wyatt feels very thankful as he looks at his grandparents.

"Thank you for taking us fishing," he says. "You were right, this is way better than video games."

That evening, they all enjoy a wonderful trout feast. Wyatt feels proud that he was able to catch dinner for his sister and grandparents. He and Grace can't wait to go fishing again.

Can you find the
hidden objects?
- 1 fishing rod
- 1 hook
- 1 bobber
- 1 secret message
- 17 fish
(Visit whitetailpress.com
for the answer)

My Fishing Story

Place a photo here of your most memorable fishing trip, and write your story below.

_____

_____

_____

_____

_____

_____

CPSIA information can be obtained
at www.ICGtesting.com
Printed in the USA
BVHW021407090719
552849BV00049B/1938/P